D1179843

SECURITY IS A THUMB AND A BLANKET

BY

CHARLES M. SCHULZ

Security
is having
someone
to lean
on.

Security
is knowing
you won't be
called on
to recite.

Security is knowing who the baby sitter is.

Security
is having
your socks
match.

**Security
is knowing
you still have
quite a few
years to go.**

Security is owning your own home.

Security
is having
the music
in front
of you.

Security is having a big brother.

Security
is sitting
in a box.

Security
is having a
good infield
behind you.

Security is having naturally curly hair.

**Security
is knowing
that big dog
can't really
get out.**

Security is having a few bones stacked away.

Security is holding the tickets in your hand.

**Security
is carrying
an extra
safety pin
in your
purse.**

Security is writing down your locker combination.

Security
is having
some friends
sleep
overnight.

Security is being able to touch bottom.

Security
is giving
the mailbox
lid an
extra flip.

Security is being one of the gang.

Security is having someone listen to you.

Security
is returning
home
after a
vacation.

Security
is having
a home
town.

**Security
is getting
to the theater
before the
box office
opens.**

Security
is knowing
there's
some more
pie left.

**Security
is hiding
an extra key
to the
back door.**

Security
is knowing
all your
lines.

Security is a candy bar hidden in the freezer.

**Security
is hearing
your mother
in the kitchen
when you
come home
from school.**

Security
is knowing
you're not
alone.

LITHO IN THE U.S.A.